CN00863078

Wes Si......

Don't Go in the Bullpen

Beautifully Illustrated by

Lauren Dobrowski

Cover Graphic Designer

Bukhari H Colombo

For Melvin and Alma Clarke

Papa & Mama

You have given us your all and we
are forever in your debt

Contents

Chapter 1

Mr Smith's Wasted Doctors Trip

Why does it always seem that your parents call you to a crisis when you are in the middle of enjoying yourself? "Wes!" Grandma called. I answered and quickly ran over to her.

"We have some nice treats for Red, can you please go and hand it to him." Said Grandma.
"Oh, and Wes do NOT go in the bullpen." She said knowingly. "No Grandma I won't."

Red was our one and a half-year-
old *pet bull*. Everyone else in the
community had dogs, cats, rabbits,
you know, normal pets but nope, not
us!

Just over a year and a half ago
Grandad decided he would adopt a
cute little calf which was now twice
my height and probably weighed as
much as our neighbour's 10-seater
minibus.

At first Grandma was not happy
when Red turned up *out of
nowhere*. On the day of Reds'
arrival Grandma was sitting on a
bench in the back garden eating
cake and having some of her
favourite red wine. The last thing
that she thought would ever
happen was having a bright red
calf, that was twice the size of our
biggest dog, appearing from behind
her unexpectedly and rubbing his
body against her leg.

Everything Grandma had in her
mouth came out like a broken fire

hydrant, including dentures. The red wine she was drinking went all over her white dress as she jumped about a foot higher than the bench she was sitting on.

"Ahhhhhhh What is that!???" screamed Grandma.

"Calm down, it's only a little baby calf." Grandad said calmly.

"I can now tell it's a calf, but what is it doing here!?" shouted Grandma angrily.

Grandad went on to explain that Red's mother had two calves and as he was the smaller one, he was being neglected as she could not nurse both calves. The farmer said he was not able to raise Red by hand because he was too busy and

didn't know what else to do.
Grandad asked the farmer if he
could have Red to take care of him
and, of course, the farmer obliged.

Grandma had no issue with Red but
was upset by the fact that
Grandad didn't talk to her about it
first. She knew this was a huge
decision, and that it would affect
everyone, and that Grandad
certainly didn't give it much
thought.

"Where would he sleep? Where
would we get milk? Who would
teach him to eat grass? Who else
in Jamaica let alone our little town,
has a pet bull that we could learn
from?" And loads of other
questions from Grandma that
Grandad could not answer.

"We'll figure it out" was all that he could say.

Once Grandad had somehow convinced Grandma that we could keep Red safely, we had to, of course give Red a "family" name.

Everyone believed Red got his name due to his colour being a beautiful bright red. However, Grandad felt it was funny to name him after Grandmas' favourite wine that she had spilt when she first met Red. His full name should be Red Tonic Wine, but as that was a mouthful, so we just called him Red.

Anyway, back to my mission to take treats to Red. I was curious to see what treats Grandma had in the bag for Red. Were they smooth chocolate fudge cakes, corn

pudding or at the very least I hope it was not my favourite Devon House ice cream?!

Grandma handed me a massive bag, "here you go, and remember don't go in the pen." She said. "OK Grandma I know, I won't."

Before I started off, I opened the bag to see what was inside. "Grandma are you sure? These treats look weird for Red". I asked. In the bag there were apples, banana leaves and pieces of a banana tree's trunk!

"Grandma, Red won't like me very much if I give him these," I said.

"He'll love it the same as how you love ice cream," said Grandma.

"Hmm, I don't know about that. They certainly don't look or smell like ice cream." I said.

"Ok, ok, go on then," said Grandma.

"Fine, I'll be 10mins," I said.

Red was now too big for our family home and was held on an open lot about a 5-minute walk away.

He loved his new home where he was free to roam on his own mini ranch, and not get told off by Grandma for trampling on the vegetable patch and eating all the nice vegetables we had planted.

His new home had lots of grass, trees to shelter under, a little pond where he could wade through and drink water, and plenty of

other animals that came to visit his pond that he could interact with.

He was the king of his own little domain and he loved every bit of his new home.

At first, I was not happy when he was relocated, as the reasons that drove us to find him a new home were in my opinion, pointless.

I let myself out the front gate of our home and started my short journey on the main road.

I passed my neighbour Mr Smith who lived across from us and was as always, busy cutting his lawn. I tried to get his attention to say good morning, but his lawnmower was so loud that even a train passing at full speed wouldn't have gotten his attention.

His lawn was huge and even had grass growing over the pavement that ran along his fence next to the road which also needed to be cut. Just seemed to me like all this grass cutting was a lot of work that could easily be avoided if he just got himself a pet bull.

It was on one of Mr Smith's lawn mowing days when we had our first incident that led to us having to relocate Red. I can remember the incident like it happened yesterday.

At that time Red still had the freedom to roam around the entire back and front garden of our home. He was often hanging out with me or with the dogs and just playing all sorts of silly games.

On that day for some reason, I left our front gate opened by mistake which allowed Red to sneak out, cross the road and onto Mr Smith's lawn.

Mr Smith also had his front gate opened, but in his defence, he was cutting his lawn and kept his gate opened as he had to go in and out to get his job done.

He was humming to himself and had his big ear protectors on which meant that he couldn't hear Red and surprisingly, didn't see him either. What happened later was a bit dramatic as Mr Smith's reaction seemed a little over the top in my opinion.

Red had found himself a nice patch of fresh grass that hadn't been cut as yet and was clearly enjoying his snack. He just happened to be standing less than a meter behind Mr Smith who was in his own little world and oblivious to everything that was happening around him.

Mr Smith was pulling his lawnmower backwards and after a few steps bumped into Red's head. Both were startled! Red jumped backwards and looked up at Mr Smith and just stood there staring at him.

Mr Smiths' actions were somehow
surprising. You could hear his
screams from a mile away and he
was so loud he startled me, even
though I was standing in my room
looking out the glass window at
what was happening.

I thought he would just step back
and ask Red to go back home so
that he could continue mowing his
lawn. Nope, he let go of his
Lawnmower, took off running, still
screaming, looked back, tripped

over his own legs, fell face first
into some prickly plants then
screamed even louder!

He then got back up took off again
and ran into a large avocado tree
and then fell again without moving!

I later found out that he had
fainted after crashing into the
tree.

Red remained calm throughout all this drama even though you could tell by the look on his face that he

was just as bemused as I was.

At the end of that day when things had settled down a bit, Mr Smith came over to our house to talk through what had happened.

He came straight over after getting back from the doctor's office, yes, he went doctors to get checked out! Apparently, he needed to have some of the thorns from the plants that he fell into removed from his hands, feet and all over his body.

He also needed an examination from the doctor to understand why he passed out, well I could have told him that and saved him the journey to the doctors.

To this day I still can't understand
why he got so worked up and
caused himself so many injuries.

As I said, this was one of the many
reasons why Red had to be placed
in a protected area to avoid similar
"problems".

Chapter 2

Just Too Nosey

I continued my journey by Mr
Smiths' house and could see my

other neighbour Mrs Wallace in her front garden.

In my opinion, she had always been a very nosey neighbour and would often ask all sorts of questions like where are you off to now? who are you going to see? what are you carrying?

Right on cue her squeaky voice hit
my ears with one of those very
questions. "Good morning Wes,
where are you off to now?"

"To see Red, Mrs Wallace." I said.
"Ok, be careful and don't go in the
pen," she said!

Huh?!, was she eavesdropping on
me and Grandma's conversation?
How did she know what Grandma
had said to me? Anyway, I said.
"Oh no Mrs Wallace I won't go into
the pen."

Like I said, Mrs Wallace has always
been nosey, and you guessed it; she
also had something to do with why
Red is now in a "protected area"!

I really don't know why but Red has
always drooled heavily. Everyone
could tell where Red has been, just
based on the trail of saliva he left
slithering on the floor wherever he
went.

Grandad said Red grew into this
bad habit as he was hanging around

with the neighbours' dogs and felt
he needed to pant heavily as the
dogs did in order to remain cool. It
was his way to try and fit into the
pack. Grandma felt this was
another of Grandads weird
theories that he couldn't prove.

Anyway, all this drooling caused
Grandma to ban Red from going
inside the house, as in her own
words he was causing a "slip hazard
for everyone", whatever that
meant.

Mrs Wallace wasn't around at the
time of Reds adoption, as she was
on one of her long nine months
holiday trip visiting her family in
England. She came back from
holiday right before the local
Carnival and came over to see

Grandma about sewing a special dress.

She went on and on about how this material that she had brought with her from England wasn't widely available and how she would be the only one wearing this type of print at the carnival.

Grandma was a jack of all trades and was the local fashion designer

who could make unique clothing, so
we often had people at the house
asking her to sew clothing for
them.

While Mrs Wallace was busy
talking Grandmas ear off, Red was
fast asleep having one of his many
midday naps. He had grown
accustomed to staying up with the
dogs at night that he struggled to
stay awake during the day.

Red was tucked up in the outside
storage shed where we used to
keep the lawnmower and all the
garden tools. This was his little
comfy spot and you could always
find him there.

The phone rang and Grandma told
Mrs Wallace to stay put and
excused herself from the

conversation and went to the front
of the house to talk privately.

I mentioned, Mrs Wallace was
nosey and of course couldn't help
herself when she heard noise
coming from the shed, and so she
had to get involved! Red must have
knocked something over in the
shed, and Mrs Wallace decided to
investigate to find the source of
the noise all by herself without any
help from us.

To the best of my knowledge, Mrs
Wallace had never been to the rear
of our house and never set foot
into our shed, so I was surprised
that she didn't even wait for
Grandma to come back or even ask
me if I knew what had made that
noise.

She stood up, slowly walked out the
backdoor and looked around the
back yard. She had clearly deduced

that the noise either came from inside or around the shed and headed straight there.

The door to the shed was on the side facing away from where she was standing so she couldn't see Red from that angle.

Red had started waking up and knocked over a broom with his huge frame while he was doing his stretches. This is what had caused the noise that Mrs Wallace heard.

This is when things took a turn for the worse. Mrs Wallace was just about to pull the door open when Red suddenly stepped out directly in front of her. Her mouth formed the shape to what might have been the worlds loudest screams ever, but only air came out her mouth. Her face was drained, and she looked pale, her knees buckled as she attempted to turn and run.

Instead, she fell backwards onto her back...... ouch!

At first, I didn't do anything as I was shocked by her behaviour, and I also knew that Red wouldn't hurt her, and he would just be as shocked as I was by her reactions.

Then came the screams! The screams were so loud it felt like

the sound was piercing my ears and
I had to cover them up. Red didn't
know what to do and so decided to
walk and stand directly over Mrs
Wallace. She closed her eyes and
screamed even louder; I really
didn't think that getting louder was
possible!

I knew exactly what would happen
next as he often did the same
thing to me if I got bumped to the
ground when we were playing.

Red lowered his face close to hers
and then gave her the biggest
slobbering lick I had ever seen.
There was saliva everywhere, in
her hair, over her eyes, down her
cheek, over her mouth, all down her
neck but worst of all down her
nose.

Red's timing wasn't great as Mrs
Wallace was in the middle of trying
to catch a breath of fresh air
after a long high pitch scream!
What should have been air was
replaced by "liquid"!

Now, I started panicking when I
realised that she couldn't breathe

and in fact was choking on all that slimy fluid! "Grandma!" "Grandma!" I screamed! "Mrs Wallace is choking!" "Grandma!" I screamed. "Please come quickly, I think Mrs Wallace is drowning!"

Grandma heard the commotion and burst through the back door. Our neighbour Mr Brown had also heard the screams and came hurdling over the front of his minibus at blistering speed towards the noise. Grandad, who was in the front garden planting tomatoes, appeared seemingly from nowhere! It felt like a large crowd had gathered in the blink of an eye!

"What's going on?" Shouted Grandma.

"Red, get off!" Shouted Grandad. "It's not Red's fault! He's just playing!" I said, trying to justify why Mrs. Wallace was coughing up all sorts of fluids and writhing around on the floor with Red standing over her.

It must have been a sight for
anyone who didn't witness what had
happened from the start.

"Winston, please Grab Red!"
Shouted Grandad.

In my mind, I'm thinking who's Winston? Mr Brown then stepped forward and held Red by his collar and gently pulled him to one side. Oh, Mr Brown is also named Winston! You learn something new every day, as Grandma would say.

As soon as Red was moved Grandad jumped into action. He stood over Mrs Wallace and tried to roll her unto her side. This should have been an easy task, but Mrs Wallace was still panicking, still choking, still squirming as well as stamping both feet on the ground with her eyes still firmly closed.

Grandad had a towel with him, his gardening towel, the towel he normally uses to wipe the sweat off his face! He had no option but to use that same towel to wipe Red's slimy saliva off Mrs Wallace's face!

You could have heard when she took her first massive breath from a mile away. This was followed by huge gulps of breaths and crying!

She then opened her eyes, looked up and saw everyone standing over her in shock.

By now Red was at some distance away with Winston, but even Red was also looking at her with a

puzzled look on his face. It's safe to say it took me a while to calm down before I could provide a reasonable explanation to everyone, including Mrs Wallace.

Grandma couldn't help herself and asked, "didn't I tell you to stay where you were, how did you end up in the backyard next to the shed?"

Grandad blunt as always said, "Mrs Wallace, you're too nosey for your own good sometimes."

I didn't really know what that meant until he used the same phrase to me some time later.

Mrs Wallace's explanation of what she felt happened was something out of a science fiction movie.

She said that Red had appeared
out of thin air in front of her, then
apparently hypnotised her with his

big eyes causing her to lose her
ability to speak or even scream,
and then to make matters worse he

made her knees weak so she fell on to her back.

She then said that Red vomited all over her face and he must have been eating spoilt cabbage as it tasted horrible. Yuck! she actually tasted Reds saliva I thought. She then said she didn't know what happened next as Red's hypnosis kept her on the ground and her eyes were glued shut as she felt she must have been having a really, really, really bad nightmare.

I started to wonder if we both had experienced this on the same day as what I had observed was drastically different to her version of events!

"Grandma what's hypoponosis?" I asked.

"Wes that's not the correct pronunciation, not now, this isn't the right time, I'll tell you later." Grandma said snappily. I could sense Grandma was annoyed with the whole situation.

Everyone was visible shaken; they were all out of breath and in disbelief and were trying to understand what had just happened.

Not me, I was very clear about what had happened, and it wasn't Red's fault as Mrs Wallace was trying to make out. In my opinion, it was all because Mrs Wallace was being too nosey and being overly dramatic. Red was innocent.
I thought we could all put this episode behind us, but I spent

weeks getting questioned from kids who heard different versions of the story.

"Wes, how comes Mrs Wallace almost drowned in your back yard?" "Do you have a pool?" "Do you have a pond?"

"Is it true that your Grandad had to give Mrs Wallace mouth to mouth to save her life and that Mr Wallace wasn't happy with your Grandad about him kissing Mrs Wallace?"

"Is it true that Winston had to wrestle your pet bull to the ground and put him into a headlock to get him away from Mrs Wallace?"

"Did you train a bull to act like a dog?" "Wes is a bull whisperer!"

"Can my dad bring his bull to you to be trained like a dog, as we don't have a dog, would be good to have two in one, a sort of "bulldog"?"

"*Wes why were there so many people at your house, were you having a party that went horrible wrong?*"

These kids even included names of people who were not even present when this incident happened!

The last thing I wanted was all these questions, it felt like they would never stop. I even played outside less in the hope that something else would happen and everyone would forget all about this incident.

What was noticeable was the fact that we had fewer visitors to our home after the now infamous Mrs Wallace's incident.

We had an open-door policy and anyone whether friends, family or strangers were always welcomed. My Grandparents would always make sure we had more food than we needed as they were sure we would have visitors at any point during the day. We even had people called "Backpackers" coming to our house for directions and would always end up eating dinner and leaving with packed snacks and fruits.

I overheard Grandma "asking" Grandad to find a better solution as people were afraid to visit us

and she felt someone was going to get seriously hurt.

She also felt that Red seemed to be getting bigger by the minute, and the space in the backyard wasn't right for him and he needed more room to roam freely.

It's safe to say the incident with Mrs Wallace was the last straw for Red, as to why he's now in his new home and away from his original home.

Chapter 3

Neighbours Minibus

Finding a new home, relocation, safety and all things to do with Red was the talk of our house for weeks. Grandad spent a lot of time seeking out suitable places to keep Red out of danger and away from nosey, clumsy neighbours.

I kept reminding everyone that it wasn't Red who was to be blamed and it was to do with everyone else overreacting for no reason.

He didn't once hurt anyone, and in fact, they got in his way. Grandad tried to explain that other bulls that size behaved differently, and that Red was an exception to the normal behaviours of other bulls. He said people had a right to panic as their understanding of what bulls are capable of will always play on their minds when they are around Red.

Unfortunately, we weren't able to find a solution in time before the next incident occurred, and this time it was costly and affected the entire community. Yikes!

There were no barriers between our home and the neighbours next door on one side. In fact, we didn't even know where one property started and the other ended.

The kids in both homes would end up playing across either properties and would often eat wherever they

were at the time and the same
unspoken rule applied to pets.

Like I mentioned before, Red spent
most of his time hanging around
the neighbour's dogs and he got so
much like them that he even
started to wag his tail and of

course the heavy drooling. It was
intriguing and funny to watch, I
mean how could a massive bull think
he is a dog?

Grandad's view was that he didn't
have any other bulls around to
emulate and only had dogs around
since he was young so in Reds mind,
he is one of the dogs.

Grandad also said that Red didn't have a mirror to see himself and didn't know what he looked like so, in his mind, he looked just like the dogs around him.

Grandma however wasn't convinced by either view and thought that Grandad often talked nonsense at times with his theories. She would argue that "if Red thinks he's a dog then why doesn't he eat dog's food instead of eating my garden plants?!".

Grandad didn't have an answer, nor did anyone else.

I didn't know who was right but all I knew is that Red was certain he was a dog and his behaviour reflected this.

The dogs in our little community were very active at night and you could hear them chasing each other, howling, barking and doing all sorts. And of course, Red being the "*bulldog*" that he is, was heavily involved in all of this.

The yards in my community were not always well lit at night, as the light from the streetlamps only covered the main roads and the front of yards, so how Red managed to see was beyond me. In the mornings there was very clear evidence as to where Red had been. Especially if the night had been particularly dark, you would see small trees flattened as Red was not able to see things in time to avoid them. He would hit into all

sorts of stuff and run them over,
especially the banana trees.

One night we had a power cut and
there was no electricity until the
following day. As kids, we all loved
those times as we could play with
flashlights in the dark and

pretended we were on some secret
mission.

Grandad would always choose these
nights to tell us about some old
scary stories that he *personally
witnessed*, which of course didn't

impress Grandma who would always
say, do you think this is the right
time, and don't listen to him Wes,
he's just making stories up.

I don't remember getting into bed that night and must have fallen asleep on the sofa, but I remember instantly jumping out of bed from hearing a loud BANG! I was confused at first as I didn't know where I was. Grandad must have put me in bed as he often did whenever I fell asleep on the sofa.

I could hear Grandma shouting out "Mel.....!!!" "Wake up!!!" "What was that sound?" Grandma kept shouting.

Mel in this case was the name my Grandma called Grandad who was fast asleep. He didn't hear the loud BANG but heard Grandma shouting and woke up.

Grandma came into my room, "Wes are you ok?" she asked.

"Yes Grandma, what happened?" I asked? "We don't know, but it sounded like it came from next door," said Grandma. "Oh My God, I hope it isn't a gas explosion!" she exclaimed

All sorts of questions crossed my mind as well. Did an asteroid crash into our backyard? I was just reading a science book on space that talked about asteroids and this was the first question that came to mind. Was it caused by a satellite falling from orbit?

My thoughts were interrupted when all of a sudden, we heard more rustling noises and then the dreaded sound, "MOOOOO", oh no, RED!

Grandad changed out of his pyjamas into his gardening clothes in seconds, if you had blinked you would have missed the quick change.

Red's mooing got louder and more distressing. "What has he gotten himself into now," said Grandma?

It was still very dark, which meant that power was still out so the only light we had was from the lantern in the dining room. Grandma grabbed the flashlight that she had on her bedside table. I wasn't planning on missing out on what was going on, so I also grabbed my little toy flashlight that I had under my pillow in my room.

I felt scared but at the same time excited as I didn't want to miss out on any adventure. Grandad grabbed the lantern that was in the dining room and we all went towards the backdoor. Red was still mooing, and

you could still hear the rustling
noises.

I wondered if he had fallen
between the garbage bins and got
stuck and unable to get up or did
he get trapped in the house next
door? Maybe he was trying to move
the satellite or asteroid that had
fallen? I couldn't tell and kept
guessing while trying to keep up
with Grandad who was walking very
quickly even though it was very
dark.

"KAREN!" Someone with a deep
loud voice shouted and of course
startled everyone as we weren't
expecting anyone else to be lurking
about.

 "Jesus! Winston, you frightened
me," said Grandma in a very high-

pitched voice. Already, everyone was in a state of panic and I still couldn't see what was happening.

"Sorry didn't mean to scare you," said Winston "but you have to see this." continuing with his request.

"KAREN, please come out and see this," said Winston.

Karen was Mr Brown's wife, or to make things easier so you can follow the story, she was Winston's wife. "I'm coming," she said, her voice breaking through the sound of another Mooooooooooooooooooo from Red.

I came to an abrupt halt when I bumped into Grandad's back as I didn't notice that he had stopped in his tracks. "What is it Grandad?" I asked? I stepped to the side of

him and he held his hand out for
me not to go further.
Wait, what?! What I saw didn't
make sense at first. Red's head was
tilted down close to his chest and
his horns seemed to have
disappeared into Mr Brown's ten-
seater minibus.

"Red, what did you do?!," said
Grandma.

Right on queue Red mooed.
Everyone was shining their
flashlights everywhere to try and
make sense of what they were
seeing.

"Red, come-on, move, so we can see
what you're hiding," said Grandma.
But Red didn't seem to be able to
move. Grandad went next to Red
and held his shoulder and
attempted to pull him back from
the minibus, but he didn't budge.

"Come-on Red, back away," said
Grandad. "Let me help you push him
back," said Mr Brown. Both
Grandad and Mr Brown tried to
push Red away from the minibus
while Grandma was busy trying to

convince Red to back away. They
tried with all their might but
either Red was being stubborn, or
he was truly stuck. Either way, he
certainly wasn't moving.

I can't imagine what it must have
sounded like from a passer-by's
perspective with all the grunting
noise with both Grandad and Mr
Brown pushing Red and with
Grandma shouting constantly,

"come-on Red move, back away, come-on" and Red's mooing. Finally, Karen came out of the house frantically asking, "what's going on, is everyone ok???" She then saw Red stuck and had the same confused expression on her face that we all had a few minutes earlier.

To be honest we were all still very confused. Mr Brown then noticed that not only was there a dent where Red was, but in fact it seemed like the entire side had been pushed in and was at least a quarter way into the bus.

It was quite hard for everyone to see in the dark even with flashlights. I remember thinking that I didn't know this minibus was that soft. Maybe Mr Brown should have bought a stronger minibus. I bet Red only bumped into it gently. Grandma was sighing and mumbling under her breath, she was in shock just as everyone else was.

Grandad apologised to Mr Brown and asked if there was anyone inside the bus. Mr Brown said no and attempted to open the bus to see what damage was done inside.

It was now obvious to everyone what had happened, Red had crashed headfirst into the bus and by the state of the bus, he must have been going at some speed. What was he chasing? Why did he feel he could safely be going at such speed in the dark? Was he playing or was he running away from something? Did he think the

bus looked like a toy? I had so
many questions!

Mr Brown was doing all he could to
try and get into the minibus,
however, we realised the doors
were also bent and the locks were
stuck. "Oh, look this window is
missing its glass, we can get
through here," said Karen. "What
do you mean the glass is missing,"
asked Mr Brown anxiously?

Yep, you guessed it, Red had hit
the minibus so hard even some of
the windows had shattered. "Be
careful, there might still be
fragments of glass still intact and
might hurt someone," said Grandad.

He was right and Mr Brown had to
use a towel to remove the

remaining glass left in the window frame.

Mr Brown finally got into the bus. He was tall and had broad shoulders, so it took some time for him to squeeze his body through the small window. I felt queasy as I didn't think that he would be able to come back out and he would be stuck in there for eternity.

It didn't help that when he finally got through the window, he landed bottom first onto a large wooden mallet and scared the life out of everyone with his high-pitched screaming. Even Red was visibly shaken from Mr Browns screams.

Grandma and Karen rushed towards the window to see if he had fallen onto glass and had cut himself and were relieved that he had only fallen unto the mallet. Mr Brown was not happy, and he became even more distressed and started complaining, "I should be in bed sleeping, but noooooo, because of this oversize bulldog I'm now in pain. Really, did I just go through the window of my own bus?" blah

blah blah. The rest of mumbling must have been another language as I certainly didn't understand what he was saying.

We were outside for most of the night trying to get Red free and before long the sun started

peaking out over the hills, so we no
longer needed our flashlights. The
sunrise showed the true extent of
the damage and everyone just
stood and stared in disbelief. Red
had really done it this time. The
bus looked like it was involved in a
full-on two-vehicle collision and
sunk right in. There was no chance
any passengers could use this for a
while, and this affect the entire
community.

Mr Brown then realised that Red's
horn was stuck under the metal
from one of the minibus' seats,
which was preventing Red from
being able to back out. Yes, Red's
horns went through the side of the
bus and ripped a seat from the
floor, yikes!

Mr Brown asked Karen for his toolbox and was able to remove the seat to allow Red to slide his horns out.

This made a screeching noise like someone running their fingernails across a blackboard. It was horrible.

However Red was out,
"wooohooooo!" I shouted!

Grandad quickly checked Red from
head to toe to see if he had
suffered any injuries, thankfully,
apart from being stuck for such a
long while he seemed to be in good
health. He was tough as a rock.
Grandad didn't want to take any
chances and called the local vet to
make an appointment for them to
come and assess Red thoroughly.

Mr Brown's minibus wasn't as lucky.
With two massive holes in the side,
dented doors, broken locks, ripped
up seats and shattered windows!

"Where do we start," asked
Grandad?

"This is going to be costly!" said Grandma.

Personally, I was just glad Red was fine after his ordeal of being stuck in a soft minibus for that long. He was already having his breakfast, and after a few enormous portions of grass, went into his shed to sleep off his night of action.

From what I could ascertain from overhearing the frustrated conversations, and lots of huffing and puffing, the repair bill was to split between Grandma, Mr Brown and some company called insurance.

I wasn't sure what insurance was, but I know Grandad had to spend quite a bit of time trying to explain what had gone wrong. They even sent someone to Mr Brown's house to check Grandad's story. All you could hear from Grandad was, "NO WE ARE NOT lying, what's so difficult to understand that our bull ran into the minibus?!"

It took three visits for the insurance people to finally decide to help with the repairs and I was impressed by how good the end result was. In fact, the minibus had never looked better. The bus now had tinted glass windows and new velvet covered soft seats. The dents were gone, and the massive holes were no longer there.

They even painted the minibus with
a new colour, bright red! Not sure
who's idea it was to paint it red but
apparently it was to make it more
visible.

Grandad of course had his own views and was convinced that the colour would cause another accident as bulls were apparently attracted to the colour red and would often attack it. As usual, Grandma wasn't convinced and would always shake her head while mumbling just enough for Grandad to hear,

"Another one of your wild theories huh." She said with her eyes rolling.

The best news for me was the fact that the Vet was happy to declare that Red had a clean bill of health. I was right, Mr Brown did indeed have a soft minibus. All that damage and yet, Red was fine.

However, the Vet did encourage Grandad to find a suitable location for Red as he felt it wouldn't be long before he had another accident. He also said that he needed to learn how to be a bull and stop trying to act like the neighbour's dogs. Apparently, it wasn't healthy.

This was good news to Grandma's ears but disappointing for me to hear as I felt the whole thing was being blown out of proportion and none of these so-called "incidents" were good enough reasons to force us to relocate Red.

Chapter 4

Grandad on a Mission

It wasn't too long after the minibus incident that Grandad found a new home for Red. In fact, with Grandma constantly reminding him, he found a new location within days.

Of all the people to suggest the ideal location it was our nosey neighbour Mrs Wallace who came up with the solution. She was actively asking around, again not minding her own business, and was given permission by the landowner to use the property free of charge.

The property was not in use and was literally a five minutes' walk from our home. She said we were doing the landowner a favour as she wouldn't have to pay to have the land cleaned regularly, as Red would naturally keep it clean with his massive appetite.

Apparently, I was asking for too much and being very cheeky when I suggested that Red should be paid if he was going to be doing all that work.

We were quite lucky with the location being so close, and I felt better about the situation knowing that Red wasn't too far away. I was pretty certain we could still hear him mooing when he needed to get our attention.

The land was huge and even had a pond which wasn't too deep. The water only came up to cover Red's knees which was perfect. However, we or should I say Grandad had a bit of work to do to make it ready for Red. He needed to put fencing up to ensure that Red was not able to leave and cause any further incidents. I really couldn't believe they were still blaming Red for all those so-called incidents.

Grandad also needed to build gates into the fence so that we could easily go in and out. I asked Grandad if we were planning to move the shed so Red could have a place to sleep but Grandad said this wasn't necessary as other bulls slept under the stars and were perfectly safe.

He also reminded me of what the vet had stated, saying that he needed to start behaving like a bull and not a dog.

Grandad was busy, it was as if he had newfound energy rushing around planning the bullpen build.

Grandma was also excited as now
she didn't have to worry too much
about Red getting hurt or
accidentally hurting someone or
damaging something!

I was still not sure about the arrangement and had plenty of questions. Who would Red play with? Would the dogs visit him? What if he was hungry and there was nothing to eat, how would we know? What if it was raining and the trees didn't provide him with enough shelter? Where would he go? What if he got out the bullpen and went the wrong way and got lost?

So many questions that Grandma had one answer for. "Don't worry Wes, Red will be more than fine." That was her answer for all questions pertaining to Red!

One week into the *bullpen build* and Grandad felt that he was almost finished.

He just needed to do one final test to see if the gate to the pen was strong enough to keep Red inside once it was closed. He was keen on building the gate from old disused materials he had laying around the yard. He wanted to avoid spending any more money and felt that this was also a good way to upcycle.

Grandma wasn't keen and she felt that the bits Grandad needed to purchase cost as little as four small cans of Coca Cola and it wasn't worth the risk. But Grandad was confident, his own words "I'm in the zone", so he went along with his original plan to use the recycled bits.

The gate was up, a bit mismatched and looked like a jigsaw puzzle but it certainly looked strong. Grandad excitedly declared the project as completed and that Red could move

into his new home the following
day.

Grandad had asked our neighbour
Mr Brown if he could help him
guide Red to his new home. This
was going to be an untested run as
Red didn't often go out unto the
road. The last time he did Mr

Smith ended up at the doctor's, so
Grandad just wanted to have that
little extra support if needed.

That night I struggled to sleep as
it felt like my best friend was
moving far away and I wouldn't see
him again. Grandad was up earlier
than normal, and clumsily woke us
all with the noise he was making
from bumping into furniture and
from all the falling kitchen
utensils.

As we were all fully awake, we
ended up having breakfast early
and going over Grandad's plans. He
literally had with him on a torn out
blank page, full drawn out plans,
with pictures, arrows, dotted lines,
where we were all going to walk and
what we each had to do to ensure

that Red's move was safe without any *incident*.

"How long did it take you to draw this up Mel?" asked Grandma. "We're just moving him less than 200 meters down the road, not to another country! Did you really need to go through all that detail?" Grandma said sarcastically.

Grandad didn't even react, he just continued to talk us through his plans, one that if we stuck to wouldn't fail.

Before long Mr Brown was over, insisting that we did the move early as he had work to go to. Grandad took Mr Brown through his plans and he sarcastically agreed it was the best moving plans he had heard to date.

Grandad and I went to the back to get Red and without fail we found him in his little shed.

At first, Grandad struggled to get him up as he had another night of running around with the neighbours' dogs and was tired. However, as soon as he was up on all fours he was bubbling to go.

Red was doing the dog panting
thing again which was amusing to
Mr Brown but normal to us.
Grandad had prepared some of

Red's favourite food the night
before, which included flowers
from Mr Smith's garden and long
sticky water grass that Grandad
had to buy. With treats in hand,
Grandad led Red out the front
gate.

We went past Mr Smith who was standing on the other side of his fence and well away from Red. He had an anxious look on his face as if he was expecting Red to do something out the norm. I could tell Mr Smith still had his previous experience with Red on his mind, however we went by slowly.

We then went by Mrs Wallace who was standing as far as she could on her veranda. Of course, she wasn't able to keep quiet and shouted out "morning everyone, morning Red!" Which made Red stopped for a second and looked to see who was calling him and had to be coaxed back into eating his treats and ushered into following Grandad. Grandad wasn't happy and gestured to her frustratingly to stop talking!

Mr Brown cautiously walked behind Red like a bull whisperer gentle saying, "good boy, go on", which annoyed me as Red didn't need to be spoken to like one of his dogs, I mean ,how was this going to help Red to act like a Bull?

Grandma, who was at some distance behind, just walked at her leisurely pace and was all smiles, as in her eyes this day was long overdue. We were down the hill in no time and standing at the entrance to Red's newly built pen. Grandad opened the gate and went in with the food and ushered Red to follow him.

Red moved towards him but stopped as soon as his shoulders went through the gate, he then let out the loudest moooooooooooow we've ever heard and stepped back towards Mr Brown.

"What happened?" I asked. "Don't know." said Grandad.

Red was now standing tall and looked more alert than he did since we woke him up this morning. "Red looked startled." said Mr Brown. "He might be frightened of the fence." said Grandad. "Don't be silly." said Grandma who crept up on us and made everyone jump.

"Don't be silly, Red's used to fences and this isn't any different." said Grandma.

Everyone was puzzled and coming
up with all sorts of reasons as to
why they believe Red might have
stopped so suddenly and reacted
the way he did.

Grandma took the food from
Grandad and led Red to the side of

the entrance, then asked us to look around to see if Red had stepped on something sharp. We spent the next ten minutes looking over the same spot but there wasn't anything out the norm.

"Ok, let's try and get him in again." said Grandma. She wasn't going to give up and clearly wanted Red in his new space. Grandad took the food and Red followed while Mr Brown did his best dog handling impression. The same thing happened and Red let out another loud moooooooow. "Oh-My-God, I can't believe this!" Grandma said in a very weird voice.

"What's the problem?" asked Grandad?

The problem became clear very quickly.

Grandad had made an amazing plan, with drawings, briefing everyone involved, doing dry runs, de-briefing after dry runs and this new thing called visualizing but it hadn't crossed his mind to measure Red. Yep, the gate entrance was too small for Red to fit through.

I watched in amazement seeing Grandma walking off mumbling in the distance and I'm pretty certain she even managed to kick a pebble, in what I can assume was either through pure frustration or it may have been anger, who knows? All I know is that she kicked a pebble.

Grandad just stood there in disbelief and was only shaken out of his daydream when Mr Brown asked if we should bring Red back to the house until the entrance was made wider. I was elated, Red is going back home, wooohooo!

Grandad conceded and we started the short walk back home only to realise we were out of food and of course this created another problem. There wasn't anything to keep Red enticed and he was quickly distracted by our neighbour's blooming flowers, and not just any neighbour, yep, it had to be Mrs Wallace. Of all the people, it just had to be her!

"Wes, quick, run to the house, look on the side table in the passageway and you'll find the leftover treats I have for Red!" said Grandad, sounding slightly panicked.

Normally Grandad was the calm easy going one, but for some reason he was clearly uncomfortable with this situation.

I darted off towards the house, by
this time Grandma had already
gone in and was nowhere to be
seen. I got to the gate and looked
back only to see Red with his front
foot climbing up on Mrs Wallace's
fence trying to get to her flowers,
whilst Grandad and Mr Brown were
trying their best to pull him off.

It suddenly hit me just how big and tall Red had become as he towered over both men. They were struggling to move him an inch and gave up as he was clearly determined to eat as many flowers as he could.

I couldn't waste any more time and burst through the gate only to see Grandma looking at me startled, "what happened?" she asked.
"I can't stop, got to get the rest of Reds treats so we can get him back into the yard!" I said while sliding pass her at the doorway.

"Wait!" said Grandma, but I was already by the table in the passageway and wondering where the treats had gone. Did Grandad give me the wrong location? Did he used all the treats and forgot? I was confused but I knew one thing for sure, there were no treats on the table.

"Wes, what treats?" asked Grandma. "If it's the grass Red was eating on his way to his pen, then I've gotten rid of them already.

I've already spread them around in the vegetable garden as they make excellent organic fertilizers." she said proudly with a smile.

"But Grandma, Red is stuck by Mrs Wallace's fence and won't leave, and we need to get some treats, so he follows us back home." I said worryingly!

I wasn't worried about Red I was more concerned about what Mrs Wallace would do or say about this situation as the last time there was an *incident* with Red, her stories were far from what actually happened.

"This is a nightmare" I thought, and I wasn't sure how to resolve it. "Grandma what do we do?" I asked?

Grandma felt there wasn't much left in the yard to entice Red as what was available were all the bits he would not normally eat. She suggested that we both went back to see if we could help Grandad and Mr Brown encourage Red to come back home.

We didn't even get through our gates when I could hear Mrs Wallace at the top of her voice screaming, "Red get off, get off!"

"Oh My God, is Red on top of Mrs Wallace? What's going on?" I asked loudly!

As soon as we got through the front gate I could see that Red was still in the same position with his front legs on top of the fence, with his neck hanging over and his tongue wrapping around flowers, with Grandad and Mr Brown trying desperately to ease him off.

All that noise from Mrs Wallace was just her being overly dramatic as always.

We got there just in time to witness a huge section of the fence come crashing down loudly under Reds weight! "Stop! Stop! Someone please stop him!" Mrs Wallace kept shouting.

We were all startled and even Red looked panicked as he went from enjoying the sweet taste of one of his favourite snacks to suddenly being in pain from falling over and bumping his face. There was dust flying everywhere!

Red quickly got back up on his feet and in a panic ran off towards Mrs Wallace's house. This certainly didn't help as Mrs Wallace was standing directly in his path and was frozen in fear.

Then came the dreaded screams!
"Get out the way Mrs Wallace!"
shouted Grandma! Everyone was
shouting, "Red stop!". "Mrs Wallace
move". "Red!, Red!"

Miraculously, Red came to a
complete stop, millimetres away
from Mrs Wallace, who was just
standing there transfixed to the
spot. I'm almost certain both their
noses had touched; it was that
close.

Mrs Wallace was shaking and
hyperventilating, she must have
spilt water on herself as there was
loads of water running down her
legs! Red then stuck his tongue out
and licked her face before walking
back to Grandad.

Grandad apologised to Mrs Wallace and then slowly led Red out Mrs Wallace's front gate and gently ushered him up the hill and through our gate. Mr Brown walked behind Red all the way and once Red was safely in our yard with the gates firmly closed, he went home.

Grandma however, stayed behind to make sure that Mrs Wallace was

ok as she looked as if she had seen a ghost. Mrs Wallace was still standing in the same spot well after Red had gone.

Later that day, Grandma told us that Mrs Wallace was traumatised and probably needed a few days to rest. I didn't stay around to hear Mrs Wallace's version of what had happened as I was concerned about Red. One thing for sure Mrs Wallace needed to build a stronger fence as the one Red was standing on was clearly weak and he could have been badly hurt!

Grandad and I took turns to inspect Red but once again he was fine, no bumps or scratches anywhere.

Chapter 5

Surely, Not More Planning...

It took another five weeks before Grandad had all the materials to rebuild Mrs Wallace's fence.

During that time, Grandad finally measured Red and was able to adjust all the gates to make sure they were wide enough for Red to get through. Grandma kept reminding him, "you should have done that from the start, then we wouldn't be in all this trouble". Safe to say Grandma wasn't the forgetting type.

Whilst we were waiting for the materials to arrive Grandma spent a lot of time visiting Mrs Wallace to check on her to make sure she was Ok.

Grandad was adamant that we wouldn't be able to move Red until Mrs Wallace's fence was repaired, as we didn't want him wandering off again to eat more flowers. This meant Red was still at home and still pretending to be a big bulldog, which was fine by me.

It was painful going out to play with all the questioning from the other kids in the neighbourhood.

"Wes, why did Red pee on Mrs Wallace?" "Did your Grandad train Red to always give Mrs Wallace a hard time?" "Is he now called Red the fence breaker?" "Was your Grandad riding Red when he tried to jump the fence?" "Why did your Grandad not put Red in the new pen?" "Did Red head-butt Mrs Wallace?" Just question after question. It felt like it would never end.

This even carried on into school and I was getting questions not only by students but also from my teachers! For some reason, they were concerned for my safety and informed the principal who then decided to get in touch with Grandma.

Embarrassingly, Grandma had to take me to school bright and early Monday morning and we both ended up in the Principals office.

I couldn't make this up, Grandma
and I sitting in the Principals
office looking like we were about
to be told off.

The Principal could hardly believe that we had a pet bull that was getting bigger by the minute, wagged his tail, panted and drooled heavily, ran around with the dogs at night, slept mostly in the day and loved licking people's faces.

She asked if she could visit our home as she wasn't convinced by what we were saying. Grandma insisted that she came to visit the same day as our house was only just over a mile away and it wouldn't take too long.

The Principal passed Grandad fixing Mrs Wallace's fence on the way to our house and asked, "is that the famous fence?". To which Grandma gave her the don't mention it look and we continued walking!

Grandma took the Principal through the house instead of the usual path next to the house as she was worried that Red might be playing outside and could startle her.

Grandma called out to Red when we got to the backyard. He was just waking up from his morning sleep and lumbered towards the back gate, with tail wagging and saliva dripping everywhere. Yep, my Principal was surprised, and it didn't take long for her to realise that we were not making it up.

She asked if Red was always like this or if he only just started behaving this way. I was shocked when Grandma used one of Grandad's theories to answer. "He has always been around dogs, and grew up believing he was a dog, and

Adventures Of A Caribbean Kid

so does or tries to do all the things that dogs would do naturally to try and fit in." Grandma said convincingly.

Even after my Principal saw how friendly and special Red was, she still insisted that this wasn't safe, and advise that we should find a suitable home for him. It always annoyed me that people who didn't even know Red still insisted that he wasn't safe. He has never harmed anyone and sure, he accidentally damaged a few fragile things, but he was always great with people.

On the way back to school Grandad told us Mrs Wallace's fence was finally repaired and that we would look to move Red into his new home the next day. This spoilt my day and I certainly wasn't looking forward to another moving day. I still didn't see why we needed to move Red, we should be asking everyone else to behave better, and not move Red.

125

Grandma decided that she wouldn't join us on our journey back to school as she needed to stay behind to "support Grandad", which meant she would ask him a million questions to see if he had done all the things that he needed to do.

With Grandma staying behind, my Principal did all she could to try to convince me that it wasn't a great idea to have Red at our home, and that it was dangerous to have him living in the same yard as us. She went on to list some so called facts about bulls still being wild animals, even though they have been domesticated, and that you could never know for sure what a wild animal will do.

"What if he stepped on you by mistake?" "What if he's running and

his horns injure you by mistake?"
"What if you are playing and he fell
on you?". What if, what if, what if,
was all I heard all the way to
school. It was clear that she was
misinformed so I politely said to
her "Well, he's been living at home
all his life and none of these so-
called what ifs' have ever happened
so I'm pretty sure we'll be fine".
"Ok Wes, no need to be sarcastic"
she responded.

How was I being sarcastic? I'm not
even sure what part of my
statement contained any sarcasm
as I was simply stating a fact, but
I decided not to ask in case I got
another lecture.

We finally got back to school, and
it felt like we were walking for the
whole day with all her questions. I

was then asked another million questions by my schoolmates as it seemed that everyone had heard that the Principal went to my house and everyone had their own theory as to why.

All kinds of stories began to surface. "*Wes got caught skipping school and was hiding by the football field and is now in trouble!*" "*Wes was caught selling snacks at school when he knows this isn't allowed!*" "*Wes has a pet bull and it chased our Principal!*" "*Wes got into a fight!*" "*Wes didn't do his homework for a whole month!*" "*Wes keeps getting zero in his test and our Principal went to talk to his Grandma!*" "*The Principal asked Wes to bring his pet bull to school so he can teach us all how to train bulls to act like dogs.*"

These stories went on and on all afternoon.

I felt like I wanted to disappear for a while, and on top of that we were moving Red to his new home the following day.

That night, under immense pressure from Grandma, Grandad measured Red again, then measured the gate to the pen again before concluding that we were good to go.

He had the same plan as before and everyone who was involved was given a full 30-minute brief.
He also talked through what to do if things went wrong, and all the various things we should do to get us back on track.

A full 30-minutes!!!

Grandad physically had everything laid out in the passageway.

Even the treats that he would use
to entice Red to follow him were
placed on the table. Grandad had
also made what he called "blinders"
that he was planning on putting on
Reds face. These homemade
blinder things didn't convince
Grandma as she felt this was
normally used for horses and not

bulls, and she couldn't see how Grandad would get Red to wear it in the first place. She put this down as another one of Grandad's wild theories.

Grandad explained in great detail how the blinders would "fit like a glove" and that they would help Red as he wouldn't be able to see anything on either side of him and would just focus on moving forward. This way he could avoid Mrs Wallace's flowers or any other distractions that may arise along the way.

All I knew was that Grandad had thought of everything, and how to deal with anything that he felt could go wrong. He had a different plan for seemingly every possible scenario. Personally, I had forgotten most of what he had asked me to do, just too much information. I planned on asking him to quickly go over my bits of the move in the morning anyway so had it covered....I thought!

"Wes, wake up," said Grandad, in a gentle but excited voice.

Not sure what time I fell asleep, but I'm guessing it must have been around the same time I overheard Grandad talking through the plans *again* with Grandma.

I checked the time and it was still early, but Grandad insisted on us getting up a bit earlier to have breakfast and to make sure we were all ready to go and understood our roles.

Again, Grandad talked me through what I needed to do. Mr Brown came over after breakfast and made Grandad aware that he was ready to go when we were. It felt like déjà vu, we even had the same breakfast as we had the last time. This time though, Grandad made sure he had enough treats just in case.

Same as before Grandad and I went to get Red. We went through the back door with lots of treats in hand as well as extra treats in the rucksack I was wearing just in case we needed them.

"Red, wake up!" shouted Grandad quite eagerly.

"Red! Come on Red, wake up!" But there was no noise, no rustling,

which was unusual as he would
normally be moving around by now
even if he was tired.

Grandad eased past me and
reached for the shed door handle.
The door creaked open and we both
looked at each other in total shock!
It was empty! What the.....! "I must
still be dreaming" I thought to
myself. Red was always in the shed
at this time, how can it be empty?

Then it hit me, oh my God where
could he be? What has happened?
Was he lost and couldn't find his
way home? Kidnapped? Injured and
couldn't move? Did he run away? A
million questions crossed my mind
all at once. I could feel myself
getting hot and sweaty from all the
worry.

Grandad looked as if he was also
having the same thoughts. "I don't
understand, he must be close by."
said Grandad.

"What's taking you all so long?" shouted Grandma in the distance. "Reds not in the shed!" Grandad shouted back.

We all panicked for a moment trying to figure out where he had gone. Finally, we calmed down and decided we would just search both yards.

We found him in less than 5 minutes and the panic was over almost as quickly as it had begun! Mr Brown called us over to his backyard and asked us to come quietly. Red was lying on his side fast asleep with one of Mr Brown's dog lying on his neck and the other dog lying on his hind legs.

They all clearly had a busy night of
running around and were fast
asleep.

We just stared quietly and in awe
as they looked so peaceful and cute
together. We then realised they
were all remarkably close friends

and loved spending time with each other.

"See! and everyone says Red is dangerous!" I yelled with annoyance. This made everyone jump! Not only that but I also woke Red and startled the dogs who jumped up and started barking.

I really didn't mean to startle everyone; it just came out. Red was up in a flash and looked dazed and not quite sure of where he was. "Calm down Red." Grandad said gently.

Grandma gave me the stare as if to say, don't say another word or else you'll be in big trouble! Red slowly woke up properly and in no time was trying to lick everyone's face.

Grandad quickly gave Red some
treats for him to calm.

Red was now calm, and we all
waited uneasily as Grandad pulled
out his homemade gadget, which he
unimaginatively called,

"Bull Blinders". Grandad had a little smile on his face as he looked around proudly, however Grandma wasn't impressed, rolled her eyes and urged us to hurry up.

I took over the feeding duties from Grandad so he could fit the blinders on to Red's head. Almost instantaneously I had slop all over my arm from my fingertips to my elbow, from Red's drooling.

Grandad slowly and gently placed the "Bull Blinders" over Red's head and adjusted it to cover the sides of his eyes.

Red rolled his head side to side at first to try and get it off. The blinders were clearly uncomfortable, but with food distracting him he slowly calmed down and carried on eating.

There was a great sense of relief and even Grandma was surprised to see Red staying so calm with this contraption on his head. Grandad did a fist pump, winked at Grandma, and had a huge smile, as if to say, see told yah before taking over feeding duties.

Finally, the long-awaited walk to Red's new home had begun. This time we went through Mr Browns front gate as it was closer, and Grandad felt if he took Red through our backyard he might want to go for a nap in the shed instead.

Red was focused on the treats and closely followed Grandad's lead. I

don't think he was too worried
about where he was going, he just
kept munching and drooling all over
Grandads hand.

Mr Brown kept a close distance
behind Red and continued his
encouraging comments same as the
last move by whispering "good boy".

This continued to annoy me, but I remembered Grandma's stare, so I kept quiet! The last thing anyone needed at that moment was me causing Red to go off plan.

We got to Mrs Wallace's gate and to our surprise she was nowhere to be seen, which made the start to the day even more unusual for me. Firstly, Red wasn't in his shed and now Mrs Wallace wasn't there being nosey and asking questions. Also, Red wearing a homemade "Bull Blinder". I wasn't sure what else to expect.

We made it passed Mrs Wallace's fence and at no point did Red turn to either side to look around! Grandad's invention actually worked!

We finally got to the entrance of the pen, and you could tell everyone was slightly nervous, myself included. This was the final hurdle and if Red made it past this point, all the planning and preparation of the last few weeks would have been worth it. Even I was hoping it would work even though I didn't want Red to be relocated.

Grandad went through the gate first with plenty of treats still in hand. His pace slowed once he got inside the pen which made Red's steps even shorter and not as forceful as the last time. Slowly but surely Red made it through the gate and into the pen for the very first time. A massive YES, WOOHOO and all sorts of celebratory noises ensued.

You would have thought we won a
gold medal at the Olympics. We all
hugged and laughed as Red was
finally home and safe.

Until it dawned on me that this was
it and Red wouldn't be coming home
anymore! Grandma saw how sad I
became and reassured me this was
the right thing to do.

I went out of the pen whilst Grandad removed the *Bull Blinders* from Reds head. Grandad then left a heap of treats in a cattle trough he had made as part of his big plans. Red was headfirst in the trough munching away while everyone went out of the pen and closed the gate. We waited outside the pen to see what Red would do next.

Once the treats were finished and Red looked up, he finally realised that he was now in a totally new environment and looked puzzled. He walked towards us then saw the fence and stopped. He then looked at grandad hands for more treats, but they were all gone.

I felt sad as it felt as if we had taken Reds freedom away. He then turned and saw the pond and knew instantly that it was water. He loved water and ran off towards the pond.

We watched in amazement as he jumped right in which made a huge splash. He just kept going in and out of the pond and was clearly enjoying himself. One side of the pond had large Lilly pads and frogs were always jumping from leaf to leaf. Red waded through the water until he was in the middle of the leaves. All you could see were frogs jumping around trying their best to avoid him and croaking loudly, obviously surprised and shocked by the size of the newcomer.

We stood there and watched Red for about an hour before Grandma ushered me to go home and get ready for school. Red was more than happy in his new home which made me less nervous and happy for him. Grandma was right after all; this was the best thing for Red.

Chapter 6

Speed, Stress, Sweats

Now that you know how Red got moved to the pen, we can get back to my task of bring him his Treats. All of those *incidents* now seemed to have taken place a long time ago and were all pretty much forgotten now. Months had passed since the move and there was a new regime in place.

Grandad had done some more work on the bullpen and had put in a second entrance a bit further away from the first entrance in order to stop people from stopping by the fence to play with the *friendly Bull*. This meant Red was now farther

away from the road and a little
harder to get to.

I got to Red's lot and had to open a
large gate made of barbed wire. It
was always tricky to open, and I
had to use all of my 8-year-old
strength to undo the homemade

rubber latch used to keep the gate
attached and in place.
I wished Grandad had followed
Grandma's advice and bought a
proper latch. After a minute of
using all my muscles pushing and
pulling, it finally gave way and I was
in.

Red was now in view and his pen
was about 30 meters away. I
couldn't help but think about
whether or not Red would really
like his treats. Was Grandma sure?
Did she give me the right bag as
these didn't look anything like the
treats Grandad normally brought
for Red? Anyway, I wasn't going to
turn back now and the worst thing
that could happen is that he
wouldn't eat it and wouldn't be my
friend for a little while.

I got to the pen that was made of the same barbed wires and called out to Red, "here you go Red". I called out a few times until he walked slowly over as if to say, "I'm coming in my own time".

Looking back, just over a year before when Red was a cute little calf, he was always bouncing around and moving quickly but nowadays it was like he couldn't be bothered and took things slowly. It seemed as if he had started to really act like a normal bull now and wasn't in any rush.

I opened the bag, picked out an apple and held it out for him to eat from my hand. He quickly munched it down, but not before leaving a massive slimy trail of saliva all over my hands...., "eew Red, did you have to do that?" I said.

I gave him more apples and he chumped them down in gulps as if he didn't need to chew them. One treat down two more to go. Yes, he loved the apples but was he going to love the rest? To my surprise he ate it all, the banana leaves went down a treat and the banana tree trunk seemed to be his favourite.

Soon the treats were gone, and I could see that he wanted more but that was it. "All gone Red" I said.

At that moment I remembered what Grandad always did when he came to see Red, he would always check him over to see if he was fine, and would often use a very large hairbrush to remove any unwanted bits from Red's hair. So, of course, I thought I'd do the same thing.

I first checked Red's head which
was already facing me as he was
waiting patiently hoping for more
treats. He was very tall by now and

I could only get to his head as he
was bending towards me. I then
said, "turn to the side Red", but he
didn't want to move so I held his
head and led him to one side, which
he allowed me to do. "He is a
gentle, harmless giant" I thought
while brushing the hairs on his
large stomach.

He looked so relaxed as if he were
having a nice massage. "This isn't
dangerous" I thought. "I don't
know why everyone keeps telling me
to be careful". I tried moving him
again, but he got bored and walked
off to eat more grass. "Red, come
back here, I haven't finished" I
ordered, but he just strolled away
eating grass as he walked.

I was keen on finishing my good
deed for the day. Grandma always

said, *"make sure you do at least one good deed for the day Wes"*.

Red had looked so calm and peaceful and for some strange reason I thought that it would be a great idea to climb through the barbed wire fence on my own and into the pen. I guess I just wanted to continue making sure he was fine. Yes, me a small tiny little 8-year-old making sure a giant of a pet Bull was ok. I slowly walked over cautiously calling to Red.

I had not been that close to him since he had gotten so big without the protection of the fence. Grandad refused to allow me inside the pen as he said that if Red were to have an accident I might hurt myself in the fence as I tried to escape.

Don't Go in the Bullpen

I was a little nervous at first but once I got there, he seemed fine and didn't react to me using the large brush to get bits off him.

It felt great being so close to Red again, just like when he was living at home and was half the size that he was now. "This must be what having a nice massage feels like" I thought as I continued brushing him.

I later found out that a few days before he was chasing after a bird and tripped over a large shrub, fell and bruised his shoulder. As far as I knew, Red had never been hurt before, so this came as a bit of a surprise to me. This was the same shoulder that I was brushing so intensely, trying to get out what I

believed to be stains but they were
actually bruises from the fall.

Red showed signs of discomfort
which I had misinterpreted as
signs that he was enjoying my help.
At first, he flinched and his
shoulders shook, then he let out

heavy puffs of air from his nostrils and the last sign had me wondering why he was using his leg to dig a hole in the ground while sliding his front leg backwards.

It hadn't occurred to me that Red was angry and wasn't liking the experience, however I soon realized that he wasn't happy when all of a sudden, his back legs shot up in the air and he turned and looked at me with large red eyes and with snot and froth coming out from his mouth and nose. I remembered freezing at first, before trying to run away but not getting any traction as both my legs were still in the air from jumping backwards in fright.

When I eventually landed back on
the ground, I took off running, not
like Mr Smith but twice as fast,
probably as fast as Usain Bolt.

I was screaming my head off and
immediately remembered those

now frightful words from Grandma,
"WES DON'T GO IN THE
BULLPEN!" It was too late and now
I was going to get a serious
pounding from Red. I could hear his
hooves pounding the ground and it
was like he was breathing down my
neck.

I was running so fast that my tears were moving horizontally to the side of my face and getting stuck in my ears, which added to the problem as now I couldn't hear properly. "What the...?" I thought" "How did I get into this situation?" To make matters worse there was now the added problem of the fence which was now coming towards me at blistering pace.

I was too small to jump over it and I certainly didn't have time to stop and slowly get through it. Maybe if I shouted timeout, Red would stop for a minute. Red sounded like an angry bigger brother who was chasing his annoying little brother who had gone a step too far.

I had seconds, milliseconds even, to figure out how I would get to the other side of the fence. "I had one choice" I thought. I needed to DIVE through the small horizontal rows in the fence! This sounded like complete madness, but it was the only thought that made sense.

With my eyes blurred from the crying and the strong winds being generated from my fast running and let's not forget that I was now also temporarily deaf from all the tears clogging up my ears, I made the daring attempt and dived straight through the fence.

Miraculously I went through without even a single scratch!

How? I don't know!

I didn't have time to appreciate
the effort it took to get through
the fence as all that was on my
mind was that Red had also figured
out a way to get through the fence

and was coming after me. I was now
moving faster than Usain Bolt

himself! I could feel Red breathing
down my neck!

The walk back to my house would usually take 5 minutes, but even with my full-on sprint, the journey felt like it was taking a lifetime!

Not sure if it was my screams, or the sound of me breaking the speed barrier that alerted everyone, but I could see Grandma in the distance looking puzzled.

Mrs Wallace was also now out in the road looking in my direction. Why was she even standing there? Outside her gate at that! Wasn't she afraid that Red might trample her? I had no time to question her, in fact I was the one that made Red angry, so I was the one he was after. Mrs Wallace uttered something but I'm pretty certain I had long passed her and was pushing past my Grandma before she could finish one word from her sentence.

Mr Smith who was mowing his lawn had also heard me and stopped. He was still wearing his earmuffs and

was watching me breeze past him
with Red hot on my heels. I must
have been quite loud for him to
have heard me as he never ever

hears anyone when he is mowing his
lawn.

I stopped suddenly as Grandma grabbed onto me. "What's wrong?!" she asked looking worried.

"Red Grandma! He's behind us!

Let's go... Let's go!" I screamed

"Where? There isn't anyone or
anything behind you!" She said
sternly.

I mustered up the courage to turn
and look. But there was Nothing?!
"Where did Red go?" He was
nowhere to be seen!

"Why are you crying and why is
there water in your ears? What's
going on Wes?" Grandma asked
sounding very confused and
annoyed at the same time.

I couldn't answer as I couldn't tell
her that I went into the bullpen
despite her warning. I couldn't tell
her that I made Red so angry that

he chased me all the way home and then had somehow disappeared. I was confused. "Where did Red go?" I was certain that he was breathing down my neck!

"Wes, what happened, did you go into the pen?" asked Grandma. "Who? Me? No grandma, why do

you think I would do that?" I said unconvincingly.

"Well for one you're missing a shoe. Another clue is that you have clearly stepped into something that came from Red and could have only come from the pen. Lastly only someone getting chased and, in your case, by a large animal could run that fast and be screaming that loud!"

I had no response and all I could do was sit there with a surprised look on my face trying to understand how detective grandma had figured it all out.

"Hope you've learned your lesson Wes, do not go in the pen again!" said Grandma. "Red is getting more and more like a Bull and he won't

tolerate the old things you both
use to get up to!" she said sternly!

It got even more embarrassing as I
was so mucky that I had to be

hosed off in the front garden and on top of that I was grounded for a week without cartoons.

Safe to say "lesson learned" I thought to myself I would never ever go into the Bull Pen ever again!

"Wes! Why are you getting hosed down in the front garden?" You guessed it; Mrs Wallace had to come to our house to be nosey. "Why were you running so fast, what happened?" asked Mrs Wallace.

Just then Grandad appeared, "leave him Mrs Wallace, he clearly doesn't want to speak." Said Grandad.

Mrs Wallace apologised and went

on her way, "well I hope all is well."
she said.

I was relieved that Grandad had
told her off as I wasn't planning on
telling anyone this embarrassing
story.

Little did I know that Grandad had
witnessed the entire thing. "Wes
you're too nosey for your own good
at times." said Grandad. I finally
knew exactly what this phrase
meant.

"Mel, what happened with Wes?
Did you see anything?" Asked
Grandma.

I couldn't tell if Grandad was
smirking because he was somehow
pleased that I had learned a hard
lesson, or if he was just happy that

I escaped with my life. However, he had to compose himself before carrying on with his version of events.

He went on to tell Grandma that he was doing some work at the back of Reds pen and only saw the last bit of the *drama*. He said that before he was able to call out to me, I had already provoked Red who stamped his feet in disgust.

He said the reason why Red had kicked his back legs high into the air and why Red had motioned towards me was because Red was being bitten by ticks, and he hated it.

Grandad had realised over the past few months that Red hadn't learned how to deal with ticks and each time he was bitten by one he got frightened and his reaction was always the same. He would huff, puff, stamp his legs and then as a last resort would jump around in an attempt to rid himself of the pests....

Grandad had been using the large brush to remove ticks and any other undesirables from Red's body. He would only do this rarely, as he felt that in due time Red would learn how to manage this himself without the need for being brushed.

Anyways, he said that because Red kicked his legs into air with such force, the downward momentum made him stumble in my direction.

He then saw me jump back while pedalling in the air, once I was back on solid ground I ran off as if I had seen a ghost. He said he was laughing until he saw how speedily I was moving towards the fence and he got really worried so called out to me, but I didn't hear him, I didn't look back and just kept going.

"How that boy got through that fence I will never know" he said

sounding both concerned and relieved."

He watched me slip through the other gate like a "ninja", and even though I lost a shoe I kept running flat out!

"Didn't your feet hurt?" Grandad asked?

"No Grandad." I said feeling slightly embarrassed. I didn't even know that I had lost a shoe and I certainly didn't feel any pain as my sole intention was to put as much distance between me and Red as my legs would allow. Self-preservation was my only objective!

"Oh My God, you could have been seriously hurt Wes!" said Grandma loudly. She grounded me for a further week, so now two weeks without any TV! She also threatened to send Red away if I was to ever go into the pen again.

"But Grandma......." I protested.

"No Buts!" she said.

I felt all sorts of emotions that day. From being happy, to scared, to embarrassed, to grateful, to annoyed, but overall relieved that I wasn't hurt.

I was just getting back to feeling normal when Mr Conrod parked outside our house in his police car and blew his horn to get our attention.

What now I thought! I watched from a small opening at my window with the curtains drawn as Grandad went out to speak with him. They were talking less than a minute when all I heard was, "why do you need Wes?"!

My mouth went dry, my knees buckled, my head started to spin, and I began to see little stars as if I was about to faint.

"Why would he want to see me? He specifically called my name! Oh My God, I'm going to be locked up?

Oh My God! No, why me, why, what did I do? I panicked, I needed to hide! I needed to run away before he caught me!

"Wes!" Grandad shouted. "Wes!" They kept calling my name! I could hear Grandma and Grandad speaking but I could not make out what was being said. "Wes!" This time it was Grandma calling me. I remained silent as I could hear the footsteps getting closer to my room.

My heart was pounding louder by the minute and felt as if it was going to burst out my chest. The door opened and Grandma stepped in, "He isn't in his room." she shouted back at Grandad. She walked past me to get to the window to get a better angle to project her voice outside, "He isn't in his room." she reiterated.

Of course, she couldn't see me, I was under the bed in pools of sweat and laying in a lot of water

that I couldn't put down to just sweat.

I was certain she could hear my heart pounding as the noise was deafening. How did I manage to get myself into this situation? I was praying for a miracle to make it all stop and for things to go back to normal.

"Wes!" Grandma called out while leaving my room. I was still not answering. Why were they not protecting me? Did they want me to be locked up in jail? "This must be a nightmare" I thought "I'll wake up any minute now!" I could hear more rustling and I overheard Grandad saying, "He must be here somewhere, couldn't have gone far."

"Did you find him?" shouted Mr Conrod. This was intense, I had nowhere to go and it didn't look like they were planning on giving up. It felt like I was under this bed for over a week.

"Wes if you don't answer me and come out to me this minute you're going to be in trouble!" Shouted Grandma.

"More trouble? How could I be in more trouble than I'm in at this very moment?" This must be one of those situations where Grandad referred to as "being caught between a rock and a hard place".

I didn't know which was worse, getting locked up by the police or getting that look from Grandma. By now my tears were in full flow and I was all drenched. I slowly crawled out from under the bed and made

my way slowly in tears towards
Grandma.

The closer I got to the front gates
the louder I cried. "Why are you
crying?" said Grandma gently.

"Why are you so wet Wes?" She
asked in shock.

"Because, because I'm going to be locked, locked, locked up?" I was in such a state that I began to stutter.

"Why, what have you done to be locked up Wes?" Said Grandma.

I really didn't know but before I could answer Mr Conrod stepped in. "It's ok Wes, you're not going to be locked up, I just wanted to speak with you." he said.

I can't begin to tell you what a relief that was. "You're not going to be locked up" was the best statement I had ever heard!

However, I was still curious about why he needed to speak to me, and my mind was racing at a hundred miles per hour, I couldn't wait to hear what he had to say.

It seemed my little adventure in the bullpen had been seen by quite a few people. Mr Conrod said he was at the other side of the fence adjacent to Red's pen speaking to a neighbour when he heard the first screams.

He turned to see me just about landing on my feet, turning and sprinting at full pelt towards the fence. He couldn't quite understand why I was running and screaming as Red was standing still, there wasn't anyone else close to me and there wasn't anything obvious that would cause me to be so scared.

He also tried calling out to me when he saw me moving at

blistering pace towards the fence with no clear way of getting through it.

I definitely didn't hear anyone calling out to me as, to be honest, I wasn't focused on having any conversations with anyone at the time. I also had tears in my ears.

He said that once I got through the last gate, all he saw was a blur and dust going up the road to my house.

"Anyway, Wes, you have some natural speed we would love to tap into it. I'm here to talk to you about coming to try out for our track and field team to represent our Police youth club!" Stated Mr Conrod with his head high, chest puffed and hands on his waist.

Wait, what?! This must be a prank. So, Police Officer Conrod turning up at our gates and causing me to panic was all for him to ask me to go to a track and field trail? REALLY?! So, all this PANICKING was over nothing!

"Wes, you look annoyed, but I can assure you this will be great. We travel all over the country to compete, so you get to see all the sights, we have regular fun training sessions with lots of ice cream, you get to go on parades and get medals. What do you think?" he said.

Mr Conrod was doing all he could to convince me, but I was still annoyed that he was partly responsible for putting me through all that emotional turmoil. In fact my knees were still shaking.

Grandma stepped in before I could answer. "Of course he can go to the trials, if he gets in then it will certainly keep him out of trouble." Grandma said passionately.

"Oh, I'm sure he will get in, you should have seen him, it was like watching that cartoon with the Roadrunner." Said Mr Conrod eagerly.

"Ok Mr Conrod, I'll do my best." this was the only thing that I could come back with.

There was no way out of this, and Grandma certainly wouldn't miss an opportunity to "keep me busy". I

could see this lasting for weeks
and I wasn't looking forward to it.

"Wes, do you want to explain to us
why you were hiding under the
bed?" Grandad sure knew when to
choose the right time to jump in.
As if I wasn't embarrassed enough.
He had a knowing smile on his face,
then started snickering which
caused Mr Conrod to turn away in
laughter.

Right there and then I knew that
Mr Conrod's visiting and asking for
me was all planned, but of course
they wouldn't admit to this. I only
found out the full story sometime
later, and by some time I mean
years later!

After the incident in the pen
happened and I was safely home,

Grandad approached Mr Conrod who was on the other side of the fence and asked him for a favour. He asked Mr Conrod to drive his police car to our house and ask for me. Grandad knew that having Mr Conrod show up at our house would make me think about my actions. He felt that this was a great way to teach me a lesson. A lesson that would keep me away from Red and out of danger.

As a part of the deal, Mr Conrod suggested that I try out for the Police Youth Club track and field team. He felt that this would give me something else to focus on and help me to stay away from Red. Both men agreed, and once they got Grandma's approval the rest....well.. you just read the rest.

The lesson worked very well as the feelings that I had on that day has stayed with me since and stopped me from setting foot into Red's pen ever again.

Oh, and Red stayed the same old Red. Still wagging his tail, still drooling, still panting, still excited to see everyone, still harmless and basically still an amazing oversized Bulldog.

Don't Go in the Bullpen

Thank you:

I would like to thank all my support network. Lauren who did an amazing job illustrating all the artwork including the cover, Bo for his graphic designing skills in bringing the cover to life. Ashley, Xavier, Zayden, Dwayne, Allia, O'Neil and Laura for being eagle-eyed editors.

Most of all thanks to Mama and Papa for being absolute inspirations.

Want to get more involved in the

Adventures of A Caribbean Kid

Follow us on:

Instagram: Adventures Of A
Caribbean Kid

Facebook: Adventures Of A
Caribbean Kid

Twitter: @AdventuresOACK

Website: www.caribkid.com

Don't miss out on new releases,
engagement and competitions!

Printed in Great Britain
by Amazon